Enrichment
Book

Brian O'Doherty
Anne and Leonard Frobisher

Gill & Macmillan
Hume Avenue
Park West
Dublin 12
www.gillmacmillan.ie

ISBN: 978 07171 53886

Design: Design Image
Print origination: Carole Lynch
Internal illustrations: Kate Shannon and Sting Art
Technical drawings: MPS Limited
Consultant editor in mathematics curriculum and pedagogy: Betty Stoutt
Cover illustration: www.designbos.ie

The paper used in this book comes from the wood pulp of managed forests. For every tree felled,
at least one tree is planted, thereby renewing natural resources.

Equations on pages 3, 6, 8, 9, 12, 15, 19, 22, 25, 27, 28, 31, 36, 37, 40, 44, 47, 50, 54, 57, 61, 64, 65, 68, 71,
74, 78, 81, 85, 88 originally published by Macmillan Education Australia. Copyright Peter Maher/
Macmillan Education Australia 2011.
Macmillan Maths Problem Solving Box 3 ISBN: 978 142029 3951.

Equation on page 34, originally published by Macmillan Education Australia. Copyright Peter
Maher/Macmillan Education Australia 2011 Macmillan Maths Problem Solving Box 3 ISBN:
9781420293951

For permission to reproduce photographs, the authors and publisher gratefully acknowledge the
following:
© Alamy: 38; © Shutterstock: 67, 84.

The publishers have made every effort to contact copyright holders
but any omissions will be rectified at the next reprint.

Chapter	Strand	Page

*Access all Check-ups on our website, www.crackingmaths.ie

Practise!

1. What is the value of 7 in each of these numbers?
   a) 175   b) 2978   c) 607   d) 73428   e) 37951
   f) 236780   g) 64752   h) 9187   i) 706234   j) 47018

2. Draw notation boards to represent these large numbers.
   a) 254639   b) 173846   c) 904285   d) 347709

3. Make the largest and smallest numbers possible with the following sets of digits.
   a) 0, 4, 8, 3, 6   b) 7, 1, 5, 9, 2   c) 8, 6, 1, 7, 9, 4

4. Write these numbers in words.
   a) 17045   b) 6268   c) 58392   d) 615840   e) 207315

5. Insert the correct symbol, either < or > between each of these numbers.
   a) 7181 _____ 7118   b) 16306 _____ 13603
   c) 19919 _____ 19991   d) 32078 _____ 32087
   e) 89542 _____ 89452   f) 92258 _____ 92528
   g) 131236 _____ 132136   h) 498537 _____ 489735

6. Complete these sequences by writing down the next 2 terms.
   a) 810, 870, 930, 990, _____, _____
   b) 1950, 1870, 1790, 1710, _____, _____
   c) 17300, 18000, 18700, 19400, _____, _____
   d) 35200, 37100, 39000, 40900, _____, _____
   e) 135700, 123700, 111700, _____, _____

7. Multiply each of the following numbers by 10, 100 and 1000.

   a) 26   b) 48   c) 175   d) 3   e) 209

   f) 430   g) 647   h) 83   i) 917   j) 651

8. Divide each of these numbers by 10 and 100.

   a) 4700   b) 38000   c) 316900   d) 9800   e) 60000

   f) 49000   g) 186300   h) 3000   i) 592000   j) 83700

9. Draw notation boards to represent each of these numbers.

   a) 5.186   b) 714.8   c) 26.704

   d) 485.206   e) 614.83   f) 58.629

10. In the following decimals, write down whether the underlined digit is a hundred, ten, unit, tenth, hundredth or thousandth.

    a) 128.9<u>6</u>1   b) <u>7</u>5.263   c) 49.0<u>8</u>   d) 3<u>5</u>.1   e) 208.52<u>7</u>

    f) <u>9</u>3.048   g) <u>1</u>78.34   h) 294.1<u>6</u>5   i) 158.<u>4</u>6   j) 1<u>2</u>.956

11. Write these sets of decimal numbers in order, starting with the smallest.

    a) 6.347, 7.643, 3.476, 4.736

    b) 29.43, 23.94, 29.34, 24.93

    c) 1.409, 1.049, 1.49, 1.904

    d) 25.268, 25.826, 25.682, 25.286

12. Round these decimals to 1 decimal place.

    a) 3.54   b) 6.89   c) 1.36   d) 42.34   e) 79.15

    f) 8.91   g) 15.37   h) 61.83   i) 59.29   j) 165.62

13. Round these decimals to 2 decimal places.

    a) 1.149   b) 2.872   c) 3.594   d) 4.216   e) 5.737

    f) 6.951   g) 7.248   h) 8.635   i) 9.683   j) 28.326

Palindromic Pals

Palindromic numbers are the same forwards and
backwards, like 22, 131 and 2332.

a) How many palindromic numbers are there
   between 1000 and 3000?

b) Find the 2nd biggest 6-digit
   palindromic number
   that looks like this:

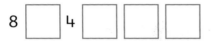

Strategy hints!

1. Look for the important words
   in the question.

2. Look for a pattern.

3. Think logically.

Extension

You can turn most numbers into a palindromic number by
adding its digits backwards. Sometimes you need to do this more
than once.

For example: The palindrome of 36: 36 + 63 = 99

The palindrome of 49: 49 + 94 = 143 and 143 + 341 = 484

a) Use this method to turn 3462 into a palindromic number.

b) Make up more problems like this one. See if a classmate can
   work them out.

1. What Could I Be?

Ellen thinks of a 5-digit number.

She says to her friends:

- The 5 digits are all different.
- The unit digit is double the ten thousand digit.
- The sum of the ten and hundred digits is 6.
- The thousand digit is the difference between the unit and the hundred digits.

Ellen challenges her friends to find what her number could be.

Pádraig says to Ellen, 'I think your 5-digit number is 15602.'

Copy what Pádraig did.

Could what Pádraig said be correct?
Explain why to a friend.

> Investigate what Ellen's 5-digit number could be.

2. More than Decimals

Patrick has 5 digit cards and a missing digits 'more than' statement.

| 0 | 1 | 2 | 3 | 4 |

Patrick tries to choose his 5 digit cards to complete the 'more than' statement so that it is correct.

0 · ☐ ☐ ☐ > 0 · ☐ ☐

This is what he did.

0 · 1 0 4 > 0 · 3 2

Copy what Patrick did.

Is what he did correct?
Explain why to a friend.

> Investigate different ways of completing the 'more than' statement correctly.

1. Make the best estimate you can for the following addition sums.
    Choose whichever method of estimating you prefer.

    a) 2649 + 1104 + 3896 + 1352   b)   4398 + 2004 + 3605

    c) 2331 + 668 + 4018 + 479   c)   8262 + 14739

    e) 2552 + 6119 + 1328   f)   2997 + 1006 + 588 + 424

2. Now use your calculator to calculate the total of each sum.
    Compare the answer to your estimate.

3. Work out the answers to these and then check them with a
    calculator.

a)	b)	c)	d)	e)	f)
3452	2859	15578	21578	6585	25163
4647	1368	12637	17296	27637	37427
+ 1368	+ 3743	+ 8194	+ 19409	+ 19476	+ 28558

4. Estimate the answers to these.

a)	b)	c)	d)	e)	f)
7024	9291	11325	15203	19649	22401
− 4648	− 5764	− 7869	− 12376	− 14873	− 19726

    g) 5204 − 1789   h)   13351 − 7679   i)   17796 − 8288

    j) 19324 − 17679   k)   23004 − 19896   l)   28115 − 24748

5. Now work out the answers with a calculator to see how accurate
    your estimates were.

6. 34967 people attended a festival on a
    Friday. A further 43278 attended the
    festival on the Saturday and 41785
    were there on the Sunday. How many
    people attended the festival over the
    3 days?

7. Mark's high score on his favourite game is 91014 points. Jack's high score is 85659 points. What's the difference between their 2 scores?

8. In its first week in the cinemas, 71203 people went to see the new blockbuster, *Pigs from Mars*. In its second week out, 58697 people went to see the film. How many more people attended the first week than the second?

Solve!   3. Operations I

Snakes and Ladders

Marco is playing Snakes and Ladders with two 6-sided dice.

He is on 41.

His last 5 moves have been + 8, +11, –15 (snake), +4, –6 (snake).

What number was Marco on 5 moves ago?

Strategy hints!

1. Look for the important words in the question.
2. Work backwards.
3. Think logically.

Extension

A player in a Snakes and Ladders game moves forward 10, then slides back 3, then moves forward 10, then slides back 3, and so on. How many moves will it take to get from 41 to 100?

1. It's ABCDE to Me

Kate makes an addition using the letters A, B, C, D and E.

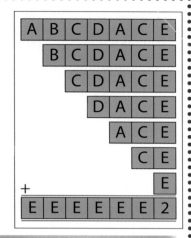

Each letter in Kate's addition stands for a different digit.

The same letters stand for the same digit.

Copy Kate's addition.

Describe any patterns you notice in the addition to a friend.

Iain, Kate's friend, says, 'I think that the letter E stands for the digit 3.'

Could what Iain said be correct?

Explain why to your friend.

> Investigate what the value of each letter could be.

2. Put a Stop to It

Eoin makes the largest possible number he can, 754, with the 3 digits 5, 4 and 7.

This is the start number for his sequence of subtractions.

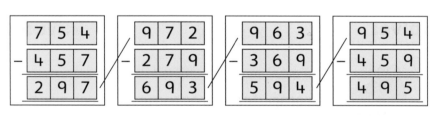

Copy Eoin's sequence of subtractions.

Describe the rule for how Eoin's sequence of subtractions works to a friend.

Check the answer to each subtraction.

Explain how you did them to a friend.

> Investigate doing what Eoin did, but with different 3-digit starter numbers.

Work out the next subtraction in the sequence.

What do you notice about the last 2 subtractions in the sequence?

Explain why Eoin's sequence stops after 4 subtractions.

1. Write down the prime numbers in the following list.

    27   19   37   45   63   79

2. Write down the composite numbers in the following list.

    13   21   33   47   73   99

3. List all of the factors of the following numbers.

    a) 12   b) 18   c) 24   d) 35   e) 40   f) 60

4. Find the highest common factor of the following pairs of numbers.

    a) 14 and 21   b) 16 and 24   c) 24 and 40

    d) 30 and 42   e) 28 and 42   f) 36 and 48

5. List the first 6 multiples of the following numbers.

    a) 4   b) 7   c) 9   d) 12   e) 15   f) 23

6. Find the lowest common multiple of the following pairs of
    numbers.

    a) 3 and 5   b) 6 and 8   c) 6 and 9

Solve! .... 4. Number Theory I

1. Computer Rules

A computer is programmed to change numbers that
are entered in according to a rule.

Here are numbers that have been entered into the
computer:

IN 6 OUT 31   IN 4 OUT 11   IN 8 OUT 59

a) Frances enters 12 into the computer. What number will come out?

b) Frances enters 15 into the computer. What number will come out?

- -

2. Computer Virus

A computer virus named Double Trouble is released. It destroys bytes on a computer's hard drive.

Each second, it wipes out twice the number of bytes that it did in the previous second.

This shows its destructive power:

Seconds	3	4	5	6
Bytes wiped	3	6	12	24

a) How many seconds will it be before the virus destroys over 1000 bytes per second?

b) How many bytes, in total, will the virus have destroyed after 2 seconds?

Investigate!

1. Prime Patterns

Luke draws a counting grid and starts to colour the prime numbers green.

row 1	1	5	9	13	17	21	25	29	33
row 2	2	6	10	14	18	22	26	30	34
row 3	3	7	11	15	19	23	27	31	35
row 4	4	8	12	16	20	24	28	32	36

Extend Luke's counting grid to 100.

Colour the prime numbers in the grid green.

Which row will never have any prime numbers? Explain why to a friend.

Which row will only ever have 1 prime number? Explain why to your friend.

Predict which row will have the most prime numbers. Explain how you decided to your friend.

> Investigate prime numbers in counting grids that have 5, 6, 7, etc. rows.

2. More and More Multiples

Sophie has 10 digit cards.

0	1	2	3	4	5	6	7	8	9

With her 10 digit cards, she tries to make five 2-digit numbers that are multiples of 2.

This is what Sophie did.

| 2 1 | 5 8 | 4 0 | 7 3 | 8 9 |

Copy what Sophie did.

Is what Sophie did correct? Explain why to a friend.

Here are 5 blank 2-digit numbers. Complete them so that each is a multiple of 2.

Explain how you did them to your friend.

> Investigate making five 2-digit multiples of 3, 4, 5, etc. using Sophie's 10 digits.

1. True or false?

    a)   An oblique line is any line that is not horizontal or vertical.

    b)   An obtuse angle is less than 90°.

    c)   Parallel lines make right angles with one another.

    d)   A straight angle is always 180°.

    e)   Horizontal and vertical lines will always be perpendicular to one another.

    f)   A reflex angle is greater than 90° but less than 180°.

2. Name the angle: acute, right, obtuse, straight or reflex angle.

    a)   115°   b) 243°   c)   18°   d)   90°

    e)   84°   f) 96°   g)   180°   h)   315°

3. Use your protractor to measure the following angles.

    a)   b)   c)

4. Use your protractor to construct the following angles.

    a) 60°   b) 110°   c) 30°   d) 160°

    e) 35°   f) 125°   g) 55°   h) 145°

5. Fill in the missing angles.

    a)   b)   c)

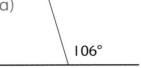 

6. Fill in the missing angles from these triangles.

   a) 56°, 83°, ?   b) 14°, 109°, ?   c) 48°, 65°, ?   d) 67°, 53°, ?

7. Now try these.

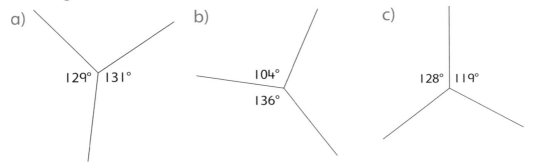

a)   129° 131°

b)   104°
      136°

c)   128° 119°

Solve!

Divided Rectangle

A rectangle is divided from corner to corner and midpoint to midpoint.

a) How many right angles can be found in the changed rectangle?

b) How many angles less than a right angle can be found in the changed rectangle?

Strategy hints!

1. Look for the important words in the question.

2. Use a drawing.

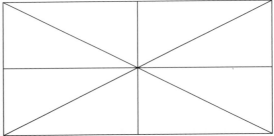

Extension

Look at the shape above.

a) How many triangles can be found in the changed rectangle?

b) Lines are drawn from the midpoint of each of the rectangle's edges to form a new shape. What shape is formed?

c) How many triangles can be found in the shape from part b)?

Investigate!

5. Lines and Angles

1. Reflex Angles

Nicola draws 3 polygons in a table.

Copy and complete the data about sides and angles in the table.

Sides			
Acute angles			
Right angles			
Obtuse angles			
Reflex angles			

Explain what is special about acute, right, obtuse and reflex angles.

Investigate drawing polygons with different numbers of reflex angles.

2. Ryan's Angles

Ryan makes 4 angles: 10°, 20°, 40° and 80°.

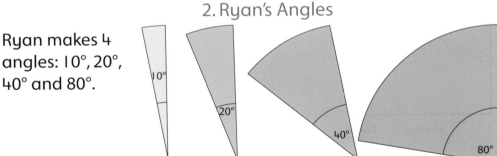

Make 1 of each angle.

Explain how you did this to a friend.

Ryan puts 2 of his angles together to make a different size angle.

How many degrees is Ryan's new angle?

Explain how you decided to your friend.

Investigate making different sizes of angle with 2, 3 or 4 of your angles.

1. This table shows the results of a survey to find the favourite activity in an adventure playground of the children in a school. Represent the information on a bar chart. Choose an appropriate scale for the numbers.

	Zip Wire	Climbing Wall	Rope Bridge	Rope Swing
Children	36	44	32	40

2. This trend graph represents the number of pupils who brought a treat to school in their lunch during the course of a week.

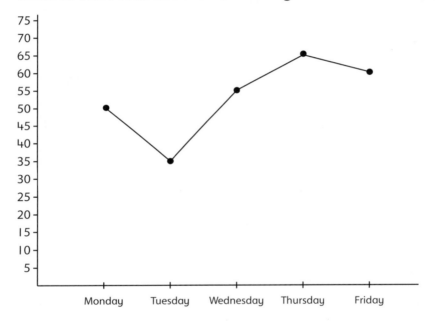

a) Which day had the second highest number of treats?

b) Which day had the second lowest number of treats?

c) What was the difference in number of treats between the day with the highest and the day with the lowest number of treats?

d) What was the total number of treats throughout the week?

e) What was the average daily number of treats?

3. Construct a trend graph to represent the following data, which describes the number of copies of *Whale-spotters' Weekly* that were sold during the course of 1 week.

Day	Mon	Tues	Wed	Thurs	Fri	Sat	Sun
Copies Sold	27	33	21	24	30	36	27

Make up 5 questions based on your graph.

Solve! 6. Data 1

Hair and Shoes

There are 42 students in our class.

Some of the students were surveyed to see if the shoes they wore on a certain day matched their hair colour.

a) What does the fraction $\frac{1}{2}$ have to do with the survey?

b) What does the fraction $\frac{19}{21}$ have to do with the survey?

	Black Hair	Brown Hair
Black Shoes	11	6
Brown Shoes	13	8

Strategy hints!

1. Look for the important words in the question.

2. Use a table or a chart.

3. Think logically.

1. Heights of Boys and Girls

Niamh's 6th class works together to find the average heights of boys and of girls in each class in their school. They make a table of their findings rounded to the nearest centimetre.

	1st Class	2nd Class	3rd Class	4th Class	5th Class	6th Class
Boys	122	128	134	140	147	152
Girls	121	126	132	138	142	148

Copy their table.

Niamh starts to draw a multiple bar chart of the average heights of boys and girls.

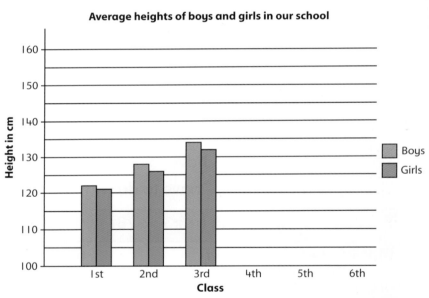

Copy and complete Niamh's multiple bar chart.

Write about what the bar chart tells you.

Investigate the average heights of boys and of girls in classes in your school.

2. Class Attendance

Adam is given the attendance of children in the 5th and 6th classes in his school for a whole week.

	Mon	Tue	Wed	Thur	Fri
5th Class	27	30	28	26	23
6th Class	29	32	26	31	28

Copy the table.

Adam says, 'The attendance in the 5th class is worse than the attendance in the 6th class.'

Could what Adam said be correct? Explain why to a friend.

Emma says, 'I am not so sure, because there are 31 children in the 5th class and 35 children in the 6th class. I think percentages should be used.'

Explain to a friend why what Emma said could be true.

Make a percentage attendance table for the 2 classes.

What does the data in the table tell you about the attendance in the 2 classes? Explain this to your friend.

Investigate which class in your school has the worst attendance record.

Practise!

1. Write equivalent fractions for each of these fractions.

   a) $\frac{1}{6}$　　b) $\frac{3}{4}$　　c) $\frac{2}{5}$　　d) $\frac{7}{8}$　　e) $\frac{5}{7}$　　f) $\frac{8}{9}$

2. Now find equivalent fractions for these fractions where the numerators and denominators are smaller.

   a) $\frac{15}{20}$　　b) $\frac{12}{15}$　　c) $\frac{16}{24}$　　d) $\frac{18}{30}$　　e) $\frac{12}{14}$　　f) $\frac{49}{56}$

3. Now change these mixed numbers into improper fractions the quick way.

   a) $1\frac{7}{12} = \frac{?}{12}$　　　　b) $2\frac{5}{8} = \frac{?}{8}$　　　　c) $3\frac{5}{6} = \frac{?}{6}$

   d) $4\frac{6}{7} = \frac{?}{7}$　　　　e) $7\frac{2}{3} = \frac{?}{3}$　　　　f) $6\frac{8}{9} = \frac{?}{9}$

4. Change these improper fractions into mixed numbers the quick way.

   a) $\frac{37}{5}$　　b) $\frac{33}{4}$　　c) $\frac{19}{2}$　　d) $\frac{61}{11}$　　e) $\frac{67}{7}$

   f) $\frac{47}{6}$　　g) $\frac{53}{8}$　　h) $\frac{87}{10}$　　i) $\frac{41}{12}$　　j) $\frac{71}{9}$

5. Work out which fraction in each of these pairs of fractions is bigger. Change the pairs of fractions so that they have the same denominators to help you.

   a) $\frac{3}{5}$ and $\frac{7}{10}$　　b) $\frac{2}{3}$ and $\frac{5}{9}$　　c) $\frac{7}{9}$ and $\frac{5}{6}$

   d) $\frac{5}{8}$ and $\frac{4}{5}$　　e) $\frac{3}{4}$ and $\frac{5}{7}$　　f) $\frac{8}{9}$ and $\frac{11}{12}$

6. Add these fractions. If your answer is an improper fraction, change it to a mixed number.

   a) $\frac{1}{3} + \frac{3}{5}$　　b) $\frac{3}{4} + \frac{1}{6}$　　c) $\frac{5}{6} + \frac{3}{8}$

   d) $\frac{1}{6} + \frac{7}{9}$　　e) $\frac{3}{8} + \frac{2}{3}$　　f) $\frac{5}{12} + \frac{5}{8}$

7. Now try these.

   a) $\frac{7}{8} - \frac{1}{6}$　　b) $\frac{5}{6} - \frac{3}{4}$　　c) $\frac{9}{10} - \frac{2}{3}$

   d) $\frac{8}{9} - \frac{5}{6}$　　e) $\frac{3}{5} - \frac{1}{4}$　　f) $\frac{11}{12} - \frac{5}{8}$

8. Now try these whichever way you prefer.

a) $1\frac{1}{4} + 1\frac{2}{3}$ b) $1\frac{1}{2} + 2\frac{2}{5}$ c) $2\frac{3}{10} + 1\frac{3}{5}$

d) $4\frac{3}{4} + 3\frac{4}{5}$ e) $6\frac{3}{8} + 2\frac{2}{3}$ f) $4\frac{5}{6} + 3\frac{4}{9}$

9. Now subtract these as mixed numbers. Don't forget to borrow from your units if you need to.

a) $4\frac{3}{4} - 2\frac{1}{8}$ b) $5\frac{1}{5} - 2\frac{2}{3}$ c) $6\frac{1}{3} - 1\frac{3}{8}$

d) $5\frac{1}{4} - 3\frac{5}{6}$ e) $7\frac{1}{10} - 4\frac{3}{5}$ f) $9\frac{1}{9} - 3\frac{5}{6}$

Solve!   7. Fractions 1

Generous Gran

A generous gran decided to give away some of her money to her relatives.

She gave $\frac{1}{2}$ of her money to her grandson.

She gave $\frac{1}{2}$ of the money left to her son.

She gave $\frac{1}{3}$ of the money left to her cousin.

She gave $\frac{1}{4}$ of the money left to her niece.

She then had €30 left and went to the cinema.

a) How much money did Gran start off with?

b) What fraction of the starting amount of money did each of the 4 relatives receive?

Strategy hints!

1. Look for the important words in the question.
2. Work backwards.

Extension

A generous friend decides to give away €32000.
To each friend, he gives away half of what he has left.
How many people will he give money to before he has €31.25 left?

1. We Are Equivalent

digit cards
alent
ement.

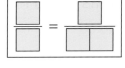

Shane chooses 5 of his digit cards to try to complete the equivalent statement correctly.

This is what he did.

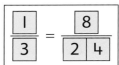

Copy what Shane did.

Is what he did correct?

Explain why to a friend.

> Investigate different ways of completing Shane's equivalent fractions statement correctly.

2. Adding 1 to Top and Bottom

Katie says, 'When you add 1 to the top and 1 to the bottom of a fraction to make a new fraction, then the new fraction is greater than the old fraction.'

Is what Katie said always true, sometimes true or never true?

Explain how you decided to a friend.

Katie shows this example to support what she said.

$$\frac{1}{2} \rightarrow \frac{1+1}{2+1} = \frac{2}{3}$$

old   new

Copy what Katie did.

Explain to your friend what Katie did to the old fraction, $\frac{1}{2}$, to make the new fraction, $\frac{2}{3}$.

Is $\frac{2}{3}$ greater than $\frac{1}{2}$? Explain why to your friend.

> Investigate adding 1 to the top and 1 to the bottom of other fractions.

1. Draw an example of each of the following shapes into your copy and label them. Colour the quadrilaterals blue and the other shapes red.

   a) Rectangle   b) Circle

   c) Pentagon   d) Isosceles triangle

   e) Square   f) Trapezium

   g) Rhombus   h) Hexagon

   i) Equilateral triangle   j) Parallelogram

2. What is the size of the missing angle in each of these triangles?

   a) 26°, 103°, ?   b) 56°, 78°, ?   c) 49°, 84°, ?

   d) 125°, 36°, ?   e) 73°, 94°, ?   f) 29°, 53°, ?

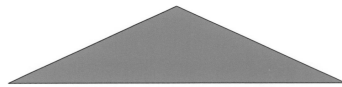

3. Construct a triangle with 1 line measuring 9cm and the 2 angles on either end of this line measuring 67° and 48°. Complete the triangle.

4. Design a tessellating pattern using a polygon of your choice.

5. Use your tangram pieces to create the following images.

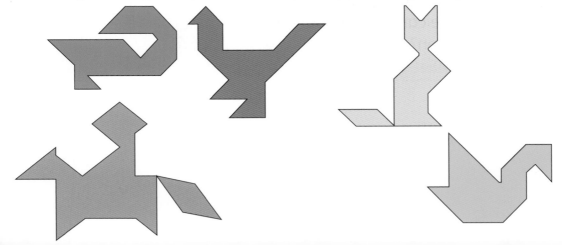

Split Hexagon

A hexagon has had its corners joined to form 6 equal sections, numbered 1 to 6.

a) Which sections can be joined to form a rhombus?

b) Which sections can be joined to form a trapezoid?

c) Which individual sections are equilateral triangles?

Strategy hints!

1. Look for the important words in the question.

2. Use a drawing.

Extension

The midpoints of sections 1 and 4 are joined.

a) How many right angles can now be found in the hexagon?

b) How many angles smaller than a right angle can now be found in the hexagon?

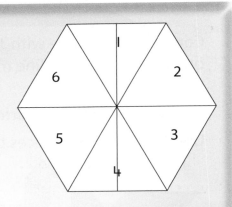

1. Sorting Quadrilaterals

Ciara has a sorting diagram for quadrilaterals.

She draws a quadrilateral in 1 of the boxes.

	0 acute angles	1 acute angle	2 acute angles	3 acute angles	4 acute angles
0 obtuse angles					
1 obtuse angle		◢			
2 obtuse angles					
3 obtuse angles					
4 obtuse angles					

Draw a copy of Ciara's quadrilateral in its box.

Explain to a friend the properties of Ciara's quadrilateral that made her draw it in that box.

> Investigate drawing a quadrilateral in each box.

2. 4 Covers 1

Olivia draws a convex quadrilateral.

She joins the middle points of its sides to make 5 polygons: A, B, C, D and E.

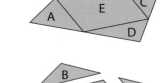

Olivia says, 'When I join the middle points of the sides of my quadrilateral, the 4 triangles A, B, C and D cover exactly the centre quadrilateral, E.'

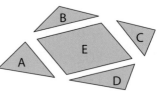

Make a copy of Olivia's quadrilateral.

Do what Olivia did to her quadrilateral.

Is what Olivia did true or false? Explain why to a friend.

> Investigate whether what Olivia said about the 5 polygons is true for other convex quadrilaterals.

1. Estimate the answers to these and then work out the answers to see how accurate each estimate is.

   a) 1203×28 b) 1003×31 c) 2502×39

   d) 2798×52 e) 3111×57 f) 4096×73

2. Now try these. Check your answers with a calculator.

a)	b)	c)	d)	e)	f)
1782	2236	2847	4085	1829	2397
× 24	× 29	× 32	× 17	× 26	× 38

g)	h)	i)	j)	k)	l)
3284	5184	4263	2538	1713	2491
× 19	× 45	× 34	× 56	× 69	× 75

3. Now try these.

   a) $3808 \div 8$ b) $7385 \div 5$ c) $4554 \div 6$

   d) $6776 \div 7$ e) $6952 \div 4$ f) $5166 \div 9$

4. Estimate the answers to these division questions by rounding up or down to the nearest ten.

   a) $279 \div 21$ b) $242 \div 28$ c) $318 \div 43$

   d) $353 \div 49$ e) $479 \div 62$ f) $541 \div 87$

5. Rewrite these division questions as multiplication questions and then work out the missing numbers. Use a rough work column to test your estimates.

   a) $102 \div 17$ b) $192 \div 24$ c) $140 \div 28$

   d) $133 \div 19$ e) $225 \div 25$ f) $144 \div 36$

6. Now try these.

   a) $368 \div 23$ b) $468 \div 18$ c) $945 \div 27$

   d) $493 \div 29$ e) $952 \div 34$ f) $722 \div 38$

7. And these.

   a) 2460 ÷ 15   b) 2682 ÷ 18   c) 6006 ÷ 22
   d) 4862 ÷ 26   e) 5214 ÷ 33   f) 8732 ÷ 37

8. If there are 16 biscuits in every packet of Rhubarb Creams, how many packets can be filled from 2820 biscuits and how many will be left over?

9. If there are 47 rows of seats and each row has 168 seats in it, how many seats are there altogether?

Solve! .... 10. Operations 2

Shortcut

Find a quick way to solve these problems.

   a) 81 x 6 – 79 x 6
   b) 178 x 6 – 173 x 6

Extension	Strategy hints!
Find a quick way to solve these problems.	1. Look for the important words in the question.
a) 66 x 7 + 35 x 7	2 Look for a pattern.
b) 1400 ÷ 28 x 2	3. Try an easier problem.

1. The Missing 8 Digit

Shannon makes the first 3 multiplications in a sequence.

| 1 | 2 | 3 | 4 | 5 | 6 | 7 | 9 | × | 9 | = _____

| 1 | 2 | 3 | 4 | 5 | 6 | 7 | 9 | × | 1 | 8 | = _____

Copy Shannon's multiplications.

| 1 | 2 | 3 | 4 | 5 | 6 | 7 | 9 | × | 2 | 7 | = _____

Work out the 3 answers.

Explain how you did them to a friend.

Extend Shannon's sequence of multiplications to 'x 81'.

Explain patterns in the sequence.

Predict what the answer will be for each multiplication in the extension of the sequence.

Explain how you decided to a friend.

Check your predictions.

> Investigate extending the sequence for x 90, x 99, x 108, etc.

2. 1s or 0s

Mark has a missing number division by 250.

[_____] ÷ 250 = _____

The digits in the missing number are either 1s or 0s.

The answer to the division is a whole number.

Mark says, 'If I choose 101 000 and divide it by 250, I get 404.'

| 101 000 | ÷ 250 = _____

Copy Mark's division. Work out the answer.

Explain how you worked it out to a friend.

Is what Mark said correct? Explain why to your friend.

> Investigate other numbers Mark could have used to complete the division correctly.

1. Spinning Wheel

Benjy goes to the fair and sees a spinning wheel.

The wheel contains 20 numbers and offers 3 prizes.

Benjy buys 3 tickets and watches as the 1st and 2nd prizes are won by tickets that he does not have.

a) What is Benjy's chance of winning the 3rd prize?

b) Benjy watches as the wheel is spun 9 times. The 3 winning ticket numbers are 4, 18 and 12. What is the chance that all 3 1st place ticket numbers will be even?

Strategy hints!

1. Look for the important words in the question.

2. Think logically.

Extension

A lucky dip box has 20 tickets in it numbered 1 to 20.

How many tickets do you need to take out of the box to be guaranteed that at least 1 is an even number?

2. Dice Roll

Zoe rolls two 6-sided dice.

a) How many different combinations can she make with the 2 dice? Remember, a roll of 4 and 6 is different to a roll of 6 and 4.

b) What is the chance that she will roll a total of 4 or lower with the 2 dice?

c) What is the chance that she will roll a total that starts with the letter 't' with the 2 dice?

d) What is the chance that she will roll a total that is in the 3 times table with the 2 dice?

3. Decks of Cards

2 decks of playing cards, with the jokers removed, are shuffled and then put into a pile in the middle of a table.

What is the chance of taking a card and it being a black ace?

1. Red, Yellow or Blue

Séamus has 2 spinners.

He spins the arrow on spinner A followed by the arrow on spinner B.

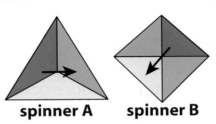

spinner A   spinner B

Séamus says, 'The chance of both arrows pointing to blue is 1 in 6.'

Is what Séamus said correct? Explain why to a friend.

Séamus says, 'The chance of both arrows pointing to red is 1 in 12.'

Is what Séamus said correct? Explain why to your friend.

Séamus says, 'The chance of 1 arrow pointing to red and the other pointing to yellow is 1 in 12.'

Is what Séamus said correct? Explain why to your friend.

> Investigate the frequency of arrows pointing to different pairs of colours when the 2 arrows are spun 50 times.

2. Connor's Dartboard

Connor has 2 squares, yellow and green.

The lengths of the sides of the yellow and green squares are in the ratio of 1 to 2.

What is the ratio of the areas of the 2 squares? Explain how you worked it out to a friend.

Connor makes a dartboard with his 2 squares.

When Connor throws a dart, it always lands in one or other of the 2 squares.

Connor says, 'The chance of a dart landing in yellow is 1 in 3.'

Is what Connor said correct? Explain why to a friend.

> Investigate the chances of a dart landing in yellow if the ratio of the lengths of the sides of the yellow and green squares is 1 to 3, 1 to 4, 1 to 5, etc.

Practise!

1. Work these out. Draw the fractions to check your answers.

   a) $\frac{1}{2}$ of $\frac{1}{6}$
   b) $\frac{1}{3}$ of $\frac{1}{4}$
   c) $\frac{1}{4}$ of $\frac{1}{4}$

   d) $\frac{1}{3}$ of $\frac{2}{5}$
   e) $\frac{3}{4}$ of $\frac{5}{6}$
   f) $\frac{2}{3}$ of $\frac{5}{8}$

2. Try these. Reduce your answers as far as you can by dividing by members of the family of 1.

   a) $\frac{2}{3}$ of $\frac{3}{4}$
   b) $\frac{3}{4}$ of $\frac{8}{9}$
   c) $\frac{5}{8}$ of $\frac{4}{5}$

   d) $\frac{5}{6}$ × $\frac{3}{4}$
   e) $\frac{4}{5}$ × $\frac{5}{6}$
   f) $\frac{8}{9}$ × $\frac{3}{4}$

   g) $\frac{6}{7}$ × $\frac{7}{9}$
   h) $\frac{3}{10}$ × $\frac{8}{9}$
   i) $\frac{4}{5}$ × $\frac{5}{12}$

3. Look for common factors of the numerators and denominators and then reduce before multiplying the fractions.

   a) $\frac{9}{10}$ × $\frac{5}{6}$
   b) $\frac{3}{8}$ × $\frac{4}{9}$
   c) $\frac{3}{5}$ × $\frac{5}{12}$

   d) $\frac{7}{9}$ × $\frac{6}{7}$
   e) $\frac{5}{12}$ × $\frac{8}{9}$
   f) $\frac{2}{3}$ × $\frac{9}{10}$

4. Now work these ones out for yourself. Remember to reduce them to their lowest terms.

   a) What fraction of 72c is 27c?   b) What fraction of 80c is 48c?

   c) What fraction of €1 is 28c?   d) What fraction of €1 is 78c?

   e) What fraction of €2 is €1.10? f) What fraction of €8 is €1.60?

5. Dominic has read 144 of the 240 pages in his book. What fraction of the book has he left to read?

6. a) Share €126 between Wendy and Sonia in a ratio of 1 : 2.

   b) Share €164 between Wendy and Sonia in a ratio of 3 : 1.

c) Share €245 between Wendy and Sonia in a ra

d) Share €413 between Wendy and Sonia in a r

e) Share €342 between Wendy and Sonia in a

f) Share €608 between Wendy and Sonia in a

7. If Ronan gave 32 Stat Attack cards to his friend and kept
for himself, in what ratio did he divide the cards?

Solve!

Number Line

A number line from 0 to 1 has been divided into
twelfths from left to right.

There are 5 points on the line called A, B, C, D and E.

- A is bigger than $\frac{3}{4}$
- B is to the left of C and it is smaller than $\frac{4}{12}$
- C is at $\frac{1}{2}$
- D is at $\frac{1}{3}$
- E is at $\frac{9}{12}$

List the points in order from left to right.

Strategy hints!

1. Look for the important words in the question.
2. Look for a pattern.
3. Use a drawing.

Extension

A different number line from 0 to 1 has been divided into tenths
from left to right.

F is at $\frac{7}{10}$, G is at $\frac{1}{5}$, H is at $\frac{4}{5}$, I is at $\frac{1}{10}$ and J is at $\frac{1}{2}$.

a) List the points in order from left to right.

b) What is the sum of the 5 points?

1. Casey's Multiplications

Casey has 9 digit cards and a missing digits multiplication of fractions statement.

Casey uses 4 of his digit cards to complete the multiplication.

$$\frac{\square}{\square} \times \frac{\square}{\square} = 1$$

This is what he did.

Copy what Casey did.

$$\frac{3}{2} \times \frac{6}{9} = 1$$

Is what he did correct?
Explain why to a friend.

Investigate other ways of completing Casey's multiplication statement using 4 digits.

2. The Missing 6

Caitríona has 10 digit cards and a missing digits fraction calculation.

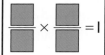

She uses 6 of her digit cards to complete the calculation correctly.

$$\frac{\square}{\square} \text{ of } \boxed{\square\,\square} = \boxed{\square\,\square}$$

This is what she did.

Copy what Caitríona did.

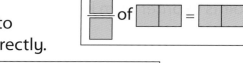

$$\frac{1}{2} \text{ of } \boxed{6\,8} = \boxed{3\,4}$$

Is what she did correct?
Explain why to a friend.

Investigate ways of completing the statement correctly using 6 digit cards.

Practise!   13. 2-D Shapes 2

1. Using your compass, construct circles with the following radii.

    a) 3cm   b) 5cm   c) 3.4cm   d) 4.2cm   e) 5.6cm

2. Using your compass, construct circles with the following diameters.

    a) 8cm   b) 12cm   c) 9cm   d) 13cm   e) 8.8cm

3. Now use a piece of string to measure the circumferences of the circles you have constructed.
    In each case, divide the circumference by the diameter of that circle. Compare your answers.

4. a) Write the letters of your town in capital letters. How many of the letters in the name are symmetrical?

    b) Now try it for the name of your county.

    c) Can you find the county with the most symmetrical letters in its name?

5. Find 3 digit numbers that have more than 1 line of symmetry.

6. Plot the following co-ordinates on a grid using an x-axis and a y-axis and then draw the shapes.

    a) (1, 3), (2, 5), (4, 3), (5, 5)

    b) (7, 1), (10, 1), (10, 6)

    c) (2, 9), (4, 6), (6, 6), (9, 9)

7. What are the co-ordinates of the points of the triangle marked on the grid?

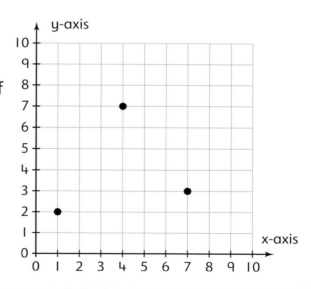

Noughts and Crosses

Nikki is playing a game of co-ordinate noughts and crosses with her friend Paige. The first player to get 3 in a horizontal, vertical or oblique row wins the game.

	A	B	C	D
3				X
2		X	O	
1	O			

Nikki is X and Paige is O.

They each make 2 moves.

It is now Nikki's turn.

Where should Nikki place her X to guarantee a win?

Strategy hints!

1. Look for the important words in the question.
2. Use a drawing.
3. Think logically.

Extension

The girls finish their game and then move on to a more challenging one.

It is Paige's turn to place her O.

Where should she place her O to guarantee a win?

	A	B	C	D
4		X	O	
3				
2				X
1	O	X		

1. Circles and More Circles

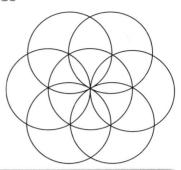

Erin draws this circle pattern.

Draw a copy of Erin's circle pattern. Explain how you did this to a friend.

How many circles did Erin use to make her pattern? Explain how you worked this out to your friend.

How many individual regions do the circles make in the pattern? Explain to your friend how you worked this out.

> Investigate colouring the pattern in different ways so that it is always symmetrical.

2. Circular Polygons

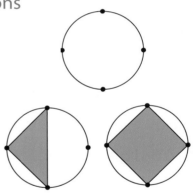

Seán draws a circle with 4 points equally spaced on its circumference.

Using the points on the circumference as corners, Seán draws 2 different polygons.

Copy what Seán did.

Seán says, 'My triangle has 2 equal sides and 2 equal angles. The angles are 45°, 45° and 90°.'

Is what Seán said about the sides and angles correct? Explain why to a friend.

What are the properties of the sides and angles of the quadrilateral that Seán drew in the circle? Explain why to your friend.

> Investigate drawing different polygons in circles with 5, 6, 7, etc. points equally spaced on their circumference.

1. Write the answer to these in your copy.
   a) 4^2 b) 9^2 c) 8^2 d) 11^2 e) 13^2 f) 16^2
   g) 19^2 h) 24^2 i) 27^2 j) 32^2 k) 39^2 l) 45^2

2. Answer these in your copy.
   a) 5 is the square root of _____
   b) 7 is the square root of _____
   c) 12 is the square root of _____
   d) 15 is the square root of _____
   e) 23 is the square root of _____
   f) 30 is the square root of _____

3. Now work out the value of these.
   a) 6^3 b) 4^3 c) 2^5 d) 18^2 e) 5^3 f) 3^4

1. Who Am I?

I am a 5-digit number.

4 of my digits are even and 1 of my digits is 0.

All of my digits are different.

I am the 5th biggest number that fits these clues.

What number am I?

Strategy hints!
1. Look for the important words in the question.
2. Think logically.

Extension

I am a 5-digit number.

All of my digits are odd.

All of my digits are different.

I am the 7th smallest number that fits these clues.

What number am I?

· ·

2. Busy Pool

A busy pool has 6 swimming lanes. There are 126 swimmers in the pool.

One afternoon, the 1st lane has twice the number of swimmers in it as the 2nd lane.

At the same time, the 2nd lane has twice the number of swimmers in it as the 3rd lane, the 3rd lane has twice the number of swimmers in it as the 4th lane, the 4th lane has twice the number of swimmers in it as the 5th lane, and the 5th lane has twice the number of swimmers in it as the 6th lane.

How many swimmers are in the 3rd lane?

Strategy hints!

1. Look for the important words in the question.

2. Use a table or a chart.

3. Think logically.

Extension

The next morning at 9:00, 21 swimmers are in the pool.

Then 3 more people dive in and some people get out.

Now there are only the amount of people in the pool that were in it at 9:00.

How many people got out of the pool?

1. Square Totals

John has 9 number cards. | 1 | 2 | 3 | 4 | 5 | 6 | 7 | 8 | 9 |

He tries to put his number cards into 3 boxes so that the total of the numbers in each box is a square number.

This is what John did.

Copy what John did.

Complete the total for each box.

| 9 | 4 |
| 3 | |

| 1 | |
| 2 | 8 |

| 5 | 6 |
| | 7 |

Is each total a square number?
Explain how you decided to a friend.

Investigate different ways of making each of the 3 totals a square number.

2. Prime Squares

Pierre de Fermat was a famous mathematician who lived over 400 years ago.

He studied pairs of square numbers whose sum was a prime number.

This is the first pair he considered.

$$1^2 + 2^2 = \underline{\qquad}$$

Complete the answer to the sum of the pair of square numbers.

Is the answer a prime number? Explain why to a friend.

This is another sum of a pair of square numbers.

$$3^2 + 4^2 = \underline{\qquad}$$

Complete the answer.

Is the answer a prime number?
Explain why to your friend.

Investigate sums of pairs of square numbers that are prime numbers.

1. Solve these equations.
    a) $123 - b = 49$
    b) $a \div 16 = 14$
    c) $m + 167 = 324$
    d) $t \times 8 = 1176$
    e) $432 \div y = 18$
    f) $z - 186 = 328$

2. Write equations for these word problems and then solve them.
    a) Betty bought a bit of butter (75g, to be precise). If the price of butter was 3c per gram, how much was the bit of butter that Betty bought?
    b) Tommy tidied his 136 toy cars into 4 storage boxes. If he put the same number of cars in each box, how many were in each box?
    c) If 13426 people live in a town and 7689 are female, how many are male?
    d) If Miserly Mick had €19024 and he decided out of the goodness of his heart to give his nephew €19, how much money did he have left for himself?
    e) Make up 2 of your own questions to try out on your classmates.

3. Work out what the variable is in each of these.
    a) $6a = 5154$
    b) $9b = 5652$
    c) $12c = 4644$
    d) $18d = 3528$
    e) $24e = 1896$
    f) $37f = 5772$

4. Use your calculator to work out these equations.
    a) $a + 3594 = 9023$
    b) $b - 1497 = 6258$
    c) $36c = 52.92$
    d) $d \div 48 = 204$

1. Letters and Numbers

a)   Y + Z = 11
     Y x Z = 24
     Y is less than Z.
     What numbers are Y and Z?

b)   P and Q are both even, 1-digit numbers.
     P is bigger than Q.
     P x Q is 20 more than P + Q.
     What numbers are P and Q?

Strategy hints!

1. Look for the important words in the question.
2. Think logically.

Extension

D, E and F are 3 different numbers. They are all less than 10.
Together, they add up to 20.
Together, they multiply to 252.
What is the difference between the biggest and the smallest of the 3 numbers?

2. Number Code

A stands for a digit from 0 to 9.
B stands for a different digit from 0 to 9.
AB + AB + A = 56

a)   What does AB stand for?

b)   Find the answer to this problem: BA − AB = ?

Strategy hints!

1. Look for the important words in the question.
2. Have a go.
3. Think logically.

Extension

K stands for a 1-digit number.
L stands for a different 1-digit number.
K x K + L x L = 85
What do K and L stand for?

1. Bank Savings

Megan and her brother Dylan each have between €20 and €50 in their bank accounts.

Megan has more euros in her bank account than Dylan has in his.

€X   €Y

Together, they have a total of €57 in their accounts.

Their older sister, Amy, says, 'I can write the total of what they have in their accounts as an equation, $X + Y = 57$. I think that $X = 25$ and $Y = 32$.'

Explain what the X and Y that Amy used in the equation mean.

Could what Amy says and thinks be correct? Explain why to a friend.

> Investigate what the values of X and Y could be.

2. Rods and Counters

Laura makes a sequence of shapes using rods and counters.

She records 3 data sequences, S, R and C, about the shapes.

Explain the table to a friend.

Shape number (S)	1	2		
Number of rods (R)	3	5		
Number of counters (C)	3	4		

Copy, complete and extend Laura's sequence of shapes and the 3 data sequences about the shapes.

Explain how you did these to your friend.

Describe to your friend any patterns you see in each data sequence, S, R and C.

> Investigate equations that relate S to R, S to C and R to C.

1. Change these fractions to decimal fractions.

   a) $\frac{9}{10}$ b) $\frac{23}{100}$ c) $\frac{538}{1000}$ d) $\frac{3}{100}$

   e) $\frac{67}{1000}$ f) $\frac{4}{5}$ g) $\frac{1}{4}$ h) $\frac{19}{20}$

2. Change these decimals to fractions and write them in their lowest terms.

   a) 0.24   b) 0.4   c) 0.75   d) 0.14

   e) 0.48   f) 0.35   g) 0.51   h) 0.625

3. Put the following decimals in order, starting with the highest in value.

   a) 4.57, 5.47, 5.74, 4.75

   b) 6.875, 7.586, 6.578, 6.785

   c) 83.26, 82.36, 82.63, 83.62

   d) 2.963, 2.693, 2.936, 3.269

4. a) 57.6 + 5.289 + 0.94   b) 13.756 + 28.47 + 365.6

   c) 4.964 + 38.7 + 3.026   d) 5.387 + 7.58 + 794.23

   e) 68.043 + 6.87 + 432.5   f) 8.14 + 75.923 + 157.9

5. a) 6.1 − 4.29   b) 34.12 − 27.396

   c) 205.7 − 163.42   d) 1.02 − 0.374

   e) 6.582 − 1.79   f) 516.27 − 58.358

6. a) 0.49 x 7   b) 2.48 x 6

   c) 36.5 x 9   d) 29.36 x 8

   e) 47.23 x 12   f) 0.859 x 4

7. a) 1.78 x 14   b) 37.6 x 17
    c) 1.478 x 26   d) 69.4 x 38
    e) 0.487 x 43   f) 83.9 x 49

8. a) 5.643 ÷ 9   b) 30.36 ÷ 4
    c) 410.2 ÷ 7   d) 69.25 ÷ 5
    e) 30.32 ÷ 8   f) 0.402 ÷ 6

9. a) 31.98 ÷ 13   b) 6.069 ÷ 17
    c) 821.6 ÷ 26   d) 21.216 ÷ 34
    e) 52.06 ÷ 38   f) 1534.5 ÷ 45

10. a) 3.57 x 1.6   b) 19.74 x 2.3
    c) 36.8 x 0.27   d) 26.41 x 3.9
    e) 45.2 x 0.28   f) 137.2 x 0.56

11. a) 3.84 ÷ 1.6   b) 13.363 ÷ 0.23
    c) 2.128 ÷ 0.28   d) 2.065 ÷ 3.5
    e) 5.365 ÷ 3.7   f) 13.018 ÷ 0.46

12. In 1 day, the Olympic torch had to be carried a distance of
    6.764km. If 19 people were selected to carry the torch and they
    each had to carry it an equal distance, how far did each person
    carry the torch?

13. Elmer the elephant weighs 358.7kg. Ernie the elephant is 1.6 times
    heavier than Elmer. How heavy is Ernie?

14. Every one of Aisling's strides is 0.68m
    long. If she walked a distance of
    94.52m, how many strides did it take
    her?

Read All About It

Today's copy of the *City Standard* newspaper contains 120 pages.

0.4 of the paper is advertisements. $\frac{1}{3}$ of the paper is sport.

0.1 of the paper is entertainment. The rest of the paper is news.

a) How many pages of the *City Standard* contain news?

b) Half of the news pages contain local news stories and half of the news pages contain overseas news stories. What fraction of the paper is devoted to local news?

Strategy hints!

1. Look for the important words in the question.
2. Make a model.
3. Think logically.

Extension

The *City Standard* varies in length each day, but its length is always a multiple of 4 pages. The Saturday paper is $\frac{1}{16}$ longer than the Sunday paper. What is the shortest length that the Sunday paper could be?

1. Fraction–Decimal Equivalence

Michael has 10 digit cards.   0   1   2   3   4   5   6   7   8   9

He uses 4 of his digit cards to complete this fraction–decimal equivalence statement.

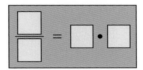

This is what he did.

Copy what Michael did.

Is what he did correct? Explain why to a friend.

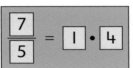

> Investigate using 4 digit cards to make more fraction–decimal equivalence statements.

2. Sums and Products

Rebecca writes an addition of 2 decimals. $3 \cdot 2 + 6 \cdot 8 = \underline{}$

What is the answer to Rebecca's addition?

Explain how you worked it out to a friend.

Rebecca calculates the product of the same 2 decimal numbers. $3 \cdot 2 \times 6 \cdot 8 = \underline{}$

What is the answer to Rebecca's product?

Explain how you worked it out to your friend.

What is the difference between the answers to the sum of the 2 decimal numbers and their product? Explain how you worked it out to your friend.

$(3 \cdot 2 \times 6 \cdot 8) - (3 \cdot 2 + 6 \cdot 8) = \underline{}$

> Investigate differences between sums and products of 2 decimal numbers whose sum is 10.

The Peckish Penguin MENU

STARTERS

Soup of the Day	€4.95
Chicken Wings	€6.95
Garlic Bread	€2.95
Warm Salad	€5.95

DESSERTS

Homemade Ice Cream	€3.95
Chocolate Brownie	€4.95
Crêpes	€7.95
Rocky Road	€5.95

MAIN COURSES

Pizza Margherita	€9.95
Pasta Bolognese	€11.95
Gourmet Hamburger	€10.95
Chicken Goujons	€8.95

DRINKS

Lemon & Lime	€1.95
Cola	€1.95
Orange Juice	€2.95
Pink Lemonade	€2.95

1. Charlotte's parents decided to have her birthday party at The Peckish Penguin. The order was as follows:

Soup x 3	Chicken Wings x 4
Garlic Bread x 2	Warm Salad x 3
Pizza x 5	Pasta x 2
Hamburger x 3	Goujons x 2
Ice Cream x 6	Brownie x 1
Crêpes x 3	Rocky Road x 2
Lemon & Lime x 4	Cola x 1
Orange Juice x 2	Pink Lemonade x 5

a) What was the total bill for the party?

b) If Charlotte's aunt paid for the drinks, what was the balance to be paid by Charlotte's parents?

c) If a service charge of 15% is added to the bill, what is the new total?

d) What change would there be out of €350?

e) Change the bill into US dollars if €1 is worth $1.29.

Solve! 18. Money

Exchange Rate

Satoshi needs to travel to Japan for a meeting. In Japan, they use yen and not euros.

Satoshi needs to take 12000 yen on his trip.

a) How much will this cost Satoshi in euros when he changes his money?

b) If the value of the yen dropped suddenly to 1 euro = 80 Japanese yen, how many euros would Satoshi save?

Exchange rate:

1 euro = 60 Japanese yen

Strategy hints!

1. Look for the important words in the question.
2. Use a table or a chart.
3. Think logically.

Extension

When Satoshi comes back from Japan, he still has 3600 yen. He changes these back into euros. The exchange rate is 1 euro = 80 Japanese yen.

The money changers take $\frac{1}{10}$ of the money in the deal and give Satoshi the rest.

How many euros does Satoshi receive in the exchange?

1. Hire a Coach

St Patrick's Primary School plans a trip for the 6th class and wants to hire a coach. O'Brien's Coaches charge €350 for the coach, plus €2 for every kilometre of the journey.

Plush Coach Company charge €300 for the coach, plus €2.50 for every kilometre.

Miss Kelly says, 'If we go on a trip that is 50km there and 50km back, the Plush Coach Company will be cheaper.'

> Investigate which company is cheaper for different distances.

Is what Miss Kelly said correct? Explain why to a friend.

2. Boxes of €1 Coins

Róisín has 10 boxes of €1 coins that she has saved.

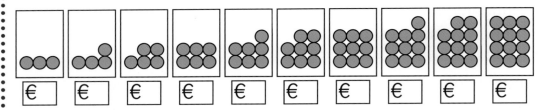

Complete the number of euros in each box.

Without opening any box, Róisín wants to give all her savings equally to a number of charities.

Róisín says, 'I can give 2 boxes to 5 charities so that they each have the same number of euros.'

> Investigate how many charities among which Róisín could share the number of euros equally.

Is what Róisín said possible? Explain why to a friend.

1. Work these out.

   a) $(39 + 26) \times 17$
   b) $186 \times (82 - 57)$
   c) $624 - (197 + 378)$
   d) $156 \div (71 - 58)$
   e) $1536 + (287 \times 8)$
   f) $4132 - (5342 - 3649)$

2. Now try these.

   a) $57 \times 19 + 1478$
   b) $304 - 928 \div 8$
   c) $5713 - 189 \times 27$
   d) $1468 + 3205 - 2659$
   e) $243 \times 474 \div 6$
   f) $1288 \div 7 + 548$

3. Put the correct symbols into these.

   a) $9 + (9 ? 4) = 14$
   b) $(6 \times 2) ? 4 = 16$
   c) $(15 - 9) ? 7 = 42$
   d) $63 ? (84 \div 12) = 9$
   e) $(9 ? 5) - 18 = 27$
   f) $108 \div (4 ? 5) = 12$

4. Find the missing symbols.

   a) $6 ? 3 ? 5 = 13$
   b) $28 ? 7 ? 9 = 36$
   c) $14 ? 7 ? 11 = 13$
   d) $8 ? 6 ? 12 = 4$
   e) $9 ? 7 ? 2 = 81$
   f) $13 ? 7 ? 9 = 54$

5. Look at these sequences of numbers. See if you can spot and describe the patterns.

   a) $1, 9, 16, 22, 27, 31, 34$
   b) $48, 46, 42, 36, 28, 18$
   c) $36, 25, 16, 9, 4, 1$
   d) $12, 27, 37, 42, 52, 67, 77, 92$
   e) $1.7, 2.1, 2.7, 3.5, 4.5$
   f) $8.3, 7.2, 6.2, 5.3, 4.5, 3.8$

6. Now spot the pattern and fill in the next 2 terms in each sequence in your copy.

   a) 19, 33, 47, 61, ___ , ___

   b) 98, 81, 64, 47, ___ , ___

   c) 9, 18, 36, 72, ___ , ___

   d) 3, 8, 15, 24, 35, ___ , ___

   e) 1.9, 3.2, 4.5, 5.8, ___ , ___

   f) 7.2, 6.4 , 6.7, 5.9, 6.2, ___ , ___

Solve!   19. Rules and Properties

Christmas Lights

Lights have been strung up in a special pattern on a Christmas tree.

Every 6th light is red. Every 7th light is green. Every 8th light is blue. Every other light is yellow.

a) What is the 1st place where there will be 2 different coloured lights in the same place?

b) How many places in the first 100 will have 2 different coloured lights in the same place?

Strategy hints!

1. Look for the important words in the question.

2. Look for a pattern.

3. Use a table or a chart.

Extension

There are 4 lighthouses on the coast near a busy shipping lane.

One lighthouse flashes every 4 seconds, one flashes every 5 seconds, one flashes every 6 seconds and one flashes every 8 seconds.

All the lights flash at the same time. How long will it be before they all flash together again?

Investigate!

19. Rules and Properties

1. Lots of 1s

Adam makes this sequence of calculations.

Copy Adam's sequence of calculations.

Complete the answers for Adam.

$$(\boxed{1\ 1} - \boxed{2}) \div \boxed{9} = \underline{\hspace{2cm}}$$

$$(\boxed{1\ 1\ 1} - \boxed{3}) \div \boxed{9} = \underline{\hspace{2cm}}$$

$$(\boxed{1\ 1\ 1\ 1} - \boxed{4}) \div \boxed{9} = \underline{\hspace{2cm}}$$

$$(\boxed{1\ 1\ 1\ 1\ 1} - \boxed{5}) \div \boxed{9} = \underline{\hspace{2cm}}$$

Explain how you did them to a friend.

Extend and complete Adam's sequence of calculations.

> Investigate patterns in different parts of the calculations.

2. Make the Sides Equal

Megan has 4 single-digit calculation statements.

Each statement has 4 missing operations in circles.

These can be +, −, x or ÷.

Copy the calculations and complete the missing operations to make the 2 sides equal.

Explain how you worked them out to a friend.

$$(\boxed{7} \bigcirc \boxed{3}) \bigcirc \boxed{5} = (\boxed{4} \bigcirc \boxed{4}) \bigcirc \boxed{4}$$
left side = ____   right side = ____

$$\boxed{1} \bigcirc (\boxed{4} \bigcirc \boxed{5}) = (\boxed{8} \bigcirc \boxed{6}) \bigcirc \boxed{5}$$
left side = ____   right side = ____

$$\boxed{2} \bigcirc (\boxed{5} \bigcirc \boxed{1}) = \boxed{8} \bigcirc (\boxed{7} \bigcirc \boxed{6})$$
left side = ____   right side = ____

$$(\boxed{9} \bigcirc \boxed{3}) \bigcirc \boxed{3} = \boxed{6} \bigcirc (\boxed{6} \bigcirc \boxed{1})$$
left side = ____   right side = ____

> Investigate making your own calculations.

Practise!

20. Length

1. Try these. Record the unit of measurement in your answer.

   a) 27mm + 3cm 4mm + 1.8cm   b) 5.9cm + 36mm + 9cm 5mm

   c) 1.47m + 296cm + 3m 28cm   d) 319cm + 1m 57+ 4.28m

   e) $3\frac{3}{4}$ km + 2km 574m + 4.867km

   f) 4.47km + 3925m + 6km 94m

2. Now try these.

   a) 203mm – 7.6cm   b) 8cm 1mm – 43mm

   c) 7m 12cm – 347cm   d) 9m 4cm – 4.79m

   e) 7.24km – 3578m   f) 8km 14m – 3.359km

3. Multiply these lengths and record the units of measurement in your answers.

   a) 16cm 4mm x 7   b) 7.8cm x 16

   c) 1m 59cm x 24   d) 276cm x 37

   e) 2km 178m x 19   f) 3.476km x 28

4. Divide these lengths and record the units of measurement in your answers.

   a) 59cm 5mm ÷ 7   b) 64.8cm ÷ 18

   c) 88m 56cm ÷ 27   d) 28.56m ÷ 34

   e) 3km 612m ÷ 14   f) 15.012km ÷ 36

5. What is the perimeter of each of the following shapes?

   a) A square with sides measuring 28cm

   b) A hexagon with sides measuring 17cm

   c) An equilateral triangle with sides measuring 36cm

   d) An octagon with sides measuring 19cm

6. Draw scaled representations of these fields into your copy. Choose a scale that you think is appropriate. Remember to write the scale under the rectangles.

a) **Field 1**

Length – 27m

Width – 15m

b) **Field 2**

Length – 24m

Width – 18m

c) **Field 3**

Length – 30m

Width – 25m

d) **Field 4**

Length – 28m

Width – 21m

e) **Field 5**

Length – 32m

Width – 20m

f) **Field 6**

Length – 40m

Width – 24m

7. Work out the perimeter of the following rectangles.

a) **Rectangle 1**

Length – 6cm

Width – 4cm

Scale – 1cm : 14cm

b) **Rectangle 2**

Length – 9cm

Width – 8cm

Scale 1cm : 6m

c) **Rectangle 3**

Length – 4.3cm

Width – 2.9cm

Scale – 1cm : 9.4m

d) **Rectangle 4**

Length – 3.4cm

Width – 1.7cm

Scale – 1cm : 2.6m

e) **Rectangle 5**

Length – 7.4cm

Width – 5.8cm

Scale – 1cm : 8.6m

f) **Rectangle 6**

Length – 9.5cm

Width – 5.5cm

Scale – 1cm : 18.4m

Scale Trail

On a map, 1 centimetre represents 25 kilometres.

a) The road trip from Westville to North Point is a distance of 331 kilometres.
How many centimetres would represent this distance on the map?

b) How many millimetres would represent a distance of 10 kilometres on the map?

Strategy hints!

1. Look for the important words in the question.
2. Make a model.
3. Think logically.

Extension

The distance between 2 towns is represented on a map by 4mm. The real distance is 130km.

How many kilometres does 1cm represent on this map?

1. Triangles and Squares

Cian has 4 equilateral triangles and 4 squares.

The sides of each triangle and each square are 10cm.

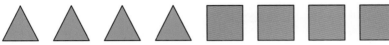

What is the perimeter of each triangle?

What is the perimeter of each square?

Explain how you worked them out to a friend.

Cian places the 4 triangles and 4 squares side to side to make a polygon.

How many sides does Cian's polygon have? Explain how you worked it out to a friend.

Cian says, 'The perimeter of my polygon is 1.3 metres.'

Is what Cian said correct? Explain why to your friend.

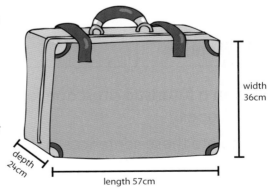

Investigate making different polygons with the 8 triangles and squares.

2. Carry-on Luggage

Shauna has a piece of luggage she wants to take on board an aircraft.

The regulations state that passengers can take luggage on board as long as the sum of the length, depth and width does not exceed 1.15 metres.

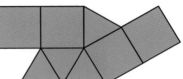

width 36cm

depth 24cm

length 57cm

Does Shauna's luggage satisfy the regulations? Explain why to a friend.

Investigate sizes of different pieces of carry-on luggage.

1. Match the net to the 3-D shape.

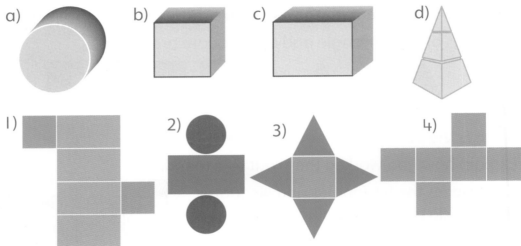

a)   b)   c)   d)

1)   2)   3)   4)

2. Fill in this table in your copy.

3-D Shape	No. of Faces	No. of Edges	No. of Vertices
Pyramid			
Cuboid			
Tetrahedron			
Cube			
Triangular prism			

3. Design a futuristic cityscape featuring different combinations of 3-D shapes.

4. Complete these sentences in your copy.

   a) A polyhedron is a 3-D shape ....

   b) A regular polyhedron is a 3-D shape ....

Curious Ant

A curious ant looks up at a square-based pyramid.

It decides to crawl along every edge of the pyramid, trying not to go over each edge more than once, if it can.

a) What is the smallest number of edges that the ant must crawl along to do this?

b) Each edge of this square-based pyramid is 5.5 centimetres long. How far will the ant crawl in its exploration?

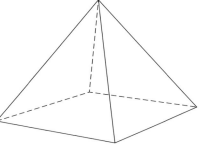

> **Strategy hints!**
>
> 1. Look for the important words in the question.
> 2. Use a drawing.
> 3. Make a model.

> **Extension**
>
> The total length of all the edges of a different square-based pyramid is 102cm.
>
> The edges of the base of this pyramid are all 10cm long.
>
> How long is each of its other edges?

1. Aoife's Prisms

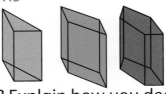

Aoife makes 3 different types of prism.

Explain to a friend why each is a prism.
Sketch a net for each prism.

What is the special name of each prism? Explain how you decided to your friend.

Complete this table about the number of faces (F), edges (E) and vertices (V).

	Number of Faces (F)	Number of Edges (E)	Number of Vertices (V)
Blue Prism			
Green Prism			
Red Prism			

Explain to your friend how you worked them out.

> Investigate relationships between F, E and V.

2. Nets of an Octahedron

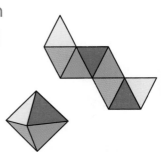

Chloe draws a net of a regular octahedron and colours the triangles.

She folds her net to make the octahedron.

Make a copy of Chloe's octahedron.

How many faces does the octahedron have?

How many edges does the octahedron have?

How many vertices does the octahedron have?

Explain how you worked them out to a friend.

Chloe said, 'I have drawn another net that folds into an octahedron.'

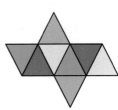

Is what Chloe said correct?
Explain why to your friend.

> Investigate drawing different nets of an octahedron.

1. Express these fractions as percentages.

   a) $\dfrac{62}{100}$ b) $\dfrac{9}{100}$ c) $\dfrac{11}{100}$

   d) $\dfrac{26}{100}$ e) $\dfrac{33}{100}$ f) $\dfrac{75}{100}$

   g) $\dfrac{98}{100}$ h) $\dfrac{87}{100}$ i) $\dfrac{44}{100}$

2. Convert the fractions to hundredths and then percentages.

   a) $\dfrac{1}{4} = \dfrac{}{100} = $ ___%   b) $\dfrac{3}{10}$ c) $\dfrac{2}{5}$

   d) $\dfrac{7}{10}$ e) $\dfrac{9}{20}$ f) $\dfrac{17}{25}$

3. Write these percentages as fractions in their lowest terms.

   a) $60\% = \dfrac{}{100} = \dfrac{}{5}$ b) 90%   c) 35%

   d) 28%   e) 38%   f) 64%

   g) 14%   h) 65%   i) 52%

4. Change these decimals to fractions and then percentages.

   a) $0.13 = \dfrac{}{100} = $ ___%   b) 0.27   c) 0.39

   d) 0.45   e) 0.03   f) 0.61

   g) 0.78   h) 0.92   i) 0.56

5. Find:

   a) 20% of 175   b) 30% of 210   c) 75% of 236

   d) 60% of 315   e) 45% of 380   f) 90% of 570

   g) 65% of 420   h) 32% of 325   i) 26% of 550

6. Write the following as percentages.

   a) 3 out of 10
   b) 4 out of 5
   c) 11 out of 20
   d) 24 out of 60
   e) 180 out of 200
   f) 45 out of 75
   g) 81 out of 108
   h) 16 out of 48
   i) 24 out of 32

7. Increase these amounts by 15%.

   a) €140
   b) €180
   c) €260
   d) €320
   e) €440
   f) €1020

8. Decrease these amounts by 60%.

   a) €280
   b) €360
   c) €395
   d) €425
   e) €655
   f) €1085

9. Calculate the percentage profit **or** loss made on each of these items.

   a) A tablet bought for €480 and sold for €360

   b) A scooter bought for €140 and sold for €98

   c) An antique bought for €250 and sold for €400

   d) A horse bought for €3600 and sold for €5220

Plumber's Bill

Bill the plumber charges €25 for 15 minutes, €40 for 30 minutes, €50 for 45 minutes or €60 for 1 hour.

Bill laid some pipes for Mr Waters and recorded the hours he worked.

How much did Mr Waters have to pay Bill?

Day	Time Worked
Monday	1 hour 30 minutes
Tuesday	3 hours
Wednesday	2 hours 15 minutes
Thursday	45 minutes
Friday	1 hour 15 minutes

Strategy hints!

1. Look for the important words in the question.
2. Have a go.
3. Think logically.

Extension

Liz the plumber has a special billing method. If you pay with cash, she gives you a $\frac{1}{10}$ discount. If you pay with a cheque, you pay the full amount. If you pay by post, Liz adds $\frac{1}{10}$ to the bill.

Mr Piper paid by post. He was charged €1210.

a) What was the bill before the $\frac{1}{10}$ was added?

b) How much would Mr Piper have saved if he had paid with cash?

1. Fractions and Percentages

Hannah has 10 digit cards and a blank fraction to percentage statement.

$$\frac{\square}{\square} = \boxed{\,} \%$$

Hannah uses 4 of her digit cards to try to complete the statement correctly.

This is what she did.

Copy what Hannah did.

$$\frac{1}{2} = \boxed{5\;0}\,\%$$

Is what Hannah did correct?
Explain why to a friend.

Investigate different ways of completing the fraction to percentage statement correctly.

2. Profit and Loss

Marcus bought a teddy bear and a rocking horse.

Each item cost between €20 and €100.

Marcus then sold the teddy bear and the rocking horse for the same number of euros.

He made a 10% profit on the teddy bear and a 10% loss on the rocking horse.

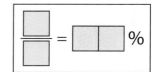

Marcus's friend, Jessica, says, 'I think the teddy bear cost you €30 and the rocking horse €40.'

Could what Jessica said be correct?
Explain why to a friend.

Investigate what the cost and selling prices of the teddy bear and the rocking horse could be.

1. Pricewatch Patty is comparing the price of towels. In 4 different shops she finds the same towel priced at €2.72, €3.16, €2.91 and €2.97. What is the average price of the towel?

2. The Ballybeg Shamrocks camogie team averaged 17 points per game on their way to winning the league title. If they played a total of 13 games in the league, what was the total number of points scored by the team?

3. The average of 3 numbers is 86. If the 1st number is 81 and the 2nd number is 87, what is the 3rd number?

4. The average of 5 numbers is 37. If the average of 4 of the numbers 38, what is the 5th number?

5. The following table details the number of km covered by Max in his car during the course of 1 week.

	Mon	Tues	Wed	Thurs	Fri	Sat	Sun
km	112	53	68	6	136	29	93

    a) What was the average number of km Max drove on weekdays?

    b) What was the average number of km Max drove at the weekend?

    c) What was the average number of km Max drove over the whole week?

1. Basketball Blitz

In 6 basketball games, Miranda averaged 10 goals per game.

In game 1, she scored 4 goals.

In game 2, she scored 12 goals.

In game 3, she scored 5 goals.

a) How many goals must Miranda have scored in games 4 to 6?

b) After game 7, Miranda's goal average went up to 11 per game. How many goals must Miranda have scored in game 7?

Strategy hints!

1. Look for the important words in the question.
2. Think logically.

Extension

Hannah scored 47 for her 5 spelling tests. Each test was out of 10.

If you removed her worst performance on any test, her average would have been 9.75.

How many 10 out of 10s did Hannah score?

2. Average Performance

5 whole numbers average 8.

1 of the numbers is 3 below average and 1 of the numbers is 3 above average.

What is the biggest that any 1 of the other 3 numbers could be?

Strategy hints!

1. Look for the important words in the question.
2. Think logically.

Extension

5 different whole numbers average 8.

All the numbers are different.

What is the biggest possible difference that there could be between the biggest number and the second biggest number?

1. Jack Calculates Averages

Jack has 9 number cards. | 1 | 2 | 3 | 4 | 5 | 6 | 7 | 8 | 9 |

He chooses a set of 3 of his number cards.

Copy the 3 number cards that Jack chose. | 7 | 3 | 8 |

Jack says, 'The average of my 3 numbers is 6.'

Is what Jack said correct? Explain why to a friend.

Complete 4 more sets of 3 numbers that Jack could have chosen, each with an average of 6.

Explain how you did this to your friend.

> Investigate sets of 2, 3, 4, 5, 6, 7 and 8 number cards, each having an average of 5.

2. Seriously Injured

Limerick Celtic played a game of Gaelic football.

The ages of the 15 players were between 20 and 35 years.

The average age was 25 years.

Sam said, 'The sum of the ages of the 15 players was 375 years.'

Is what Sam said correct? Explain why to a friend.

2 of the team were seriously injured and could not play for the rest of the game.

The team was down to 13 players.

The average age of the 13 players was 24 years.

Sam said, 'The ages of the 2 injured players are 26 and 30 years.'

Could what Sam said be correct? Explain why to your friend.

> Investigate what the ages of the 2 injured players could be.

1. Each of the following people bought a scooter priced at €50. However, none of them had enough money in their bank accounts and so they ended up overdrawn. The table below shows how much overdrawn each person was after buying the scooter. Work out how much each of them had in their account before they bought the scooter.

Name of Account Holder	Account Balance
Bob Broke	−€19.43
Sid Smashed	−€24.06
Billy Brassick	−€8.19
Sally Skint	−€36.28
Sam Spendsmore	−€14.71

2. The following table shows the total height of 6 different icebergs: the height above sea level and the depth below. Fill in the gaps in the table in your copy. The first one is done for you.

	Total Height of the Iceberg	Height Above Sea Level	Depth Below Sea Level
Iceberg 1	138m	38m	
Iceberg 2	141m		−87m
Iceberg 3		46m	−69m
Iceberg 4	103m	19m	
Iceberg 5	126m		−75m
Iceberg 6		49m	−94m

James Frond

a) Secret Agent James Frond is sending a message in a secret code.
He uses numbers to stand for letters.
The letters have been moved around slightly from their usual order in the alphabet.
His message is:

15 11 4 26 18 4   7 4 11 15!

What is James's message?

b) James receives a reply in a slightly different code. The reply is:

16 15   21 9 6   24 2 26

What is the reply?

Strategy hints!

1. Look for the important words in the question.
2. Look for a pattern.
3. Think logically.

Extension

Create your own secret code and send a message to a classmate. See if they can work it out.

1. Below Par

Lauren takes part in a golf tournament over 2 rounds.

Her scores for the 2 rounds were both between 65 and 75.

Her final total for the 2 rounds was –5.

The par score for a round was 72.

David says, 'Lauren's 2 rounds were 64 and 75.'

Could what David said be correct? Explain why to a friend.

Investigate what Lauren's score for each of the 2 rounds could be.

2. Unusual Dice

Daniel has a yellow die and a green die.

The 6 numbers on the yellow die are the positive numbers +1, +2, +3, +4, +5 and +6.

| +1 | +2 | +3 | +4 | +5 | +6 |

| –1 | –2 | –3 | –4 | –5 | –6 |

The 6 numbers on the green die are the negative numbers –1, –2, –3, –4, –5 and –6.

Daniel rolls his 2 dice.

His total of the 2 numbers shown is –1.

He says, 'My numbers are –3 and +4.'

Could what Daniel said be correct? Explain why to a friend.

Investigate what the 2 numbers shown on the dice could be.

1. Can you write these as kilograms and grams?
   a) 2047g
   b) 1980g
   c) 7001g
   d) 1.8kg
   e) 3.519kg
   f) 8.04kg
   g) 645g
   h) 9.2kg
   i) 7.046kg

2. Fill in the gaps in your copy.

g	kg g	kg
		8.12kg
	2kg 73g	
186g		
		4.078kg
	2kg 7g	

3. Now try these. Remember to change them to the same units before you start.
   a) 2789g + 3kg 185g + 1.693kg
   b) 8.05kg + 1480g + 3kg 27g
   c) 0.796kg + 5kg 78g + 942g
   d) 6kg 235g + 4.837kg + 5074g
   e) 4.268kg + 3kg 9g + 756g
   f) 2kg 316g + 0.578kg + 7206g

4. Now try these subtraction questions, also changing weights to the same unit first.
   a) 4kg 35g – 1.48kg
   b) 7201g – 3kg 54g
   c) 6.425kg – 4976g
   d) 7kg 364g – 4.785kg
   e) 5024g – 2.548kg
   f) 6kg 38g – 369g

5. Now try these.
   a) 397g x 8
   b) 2kg 563g x 9
   c) 4.74kg x 7
   d) 6kg 68g x 14
   e) 5836g x 26
   f) 8.109kg x 35

6. Now try these.
   a) 5.034kg ÷ 6
   b) 6kg 368g ÷ 8
   c) 2964g ÷ 12
   d) 21.44kg ÷ 16
   e) 8kg 763g ÷ 23
   f) 76.05kg ÷ 39

7. If 27 packets of pasta weigh 25.866kg, how much does each individual packet weigh?

8. If the total weight of the people travelling in a lift was 253.64kg and 1 person weighing 71kg 49g got out, what was the total weight of the people left in the lift?

9. There are 6 cupcakes in a box. Each cupcake weighs 0.179g. If the total weight of the box and the cupcakes is 1.35kg, what is the weight of the box when it is empty?

Solve!   26. Weight

Baby Elephants

There are 2 baby elephants at the city zoo. Zazu is 6 months old and Bazeri is 12 months old.

Together, they weigh exactly 1 ton. Bazeri weighs 190 kilograms more than Zazu.

a) How much does each baby elephant weigh?

b) 6 months ago, Bazeri weighed what Zazu weighs now. The elephants will each grow to weigh about 5 tons as adults.

If Bazeri continues to grow at the same rate, about how old will she be when she reaches her full adult weight?

Strategy hints!

1. Look for the important words in the question.

2. Use a table or a chart.

Extension

Together, the 4 rhinos at the zoo weigh 3.29 tons. Their weights all differ by the same amount.

The lightest rhino weighs 800kg. What do the other 3 rhinos weigh?

1. Kilograms to Grams

Jordan has 2 of each of the digit cards 1 to 9 and a missing digits

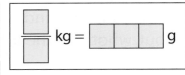

fraction of kilograms to grams statement.

Jordan uses 5 of his digit cards to complete the statement correctly to the nearest gram.

This is what he did.

$$\frac{1}{7} \text{ kg} = \boxed{1}\boxed{4}\boxed{3} \text{ g}$$

Copy what Jordan did.

Is what he did correct? Explain why to a friend.

> Investigate different ways of completing the kilograms to grams statement correctly.

2. Weight of a Brick

Sinéad has a pair of scales.

On the left pan, Sinéad puts a weight and one-third of a brick.

On the right pan, she puts a whole brick so that the scales balance.

Sinéad says, 'If my weight on the left pan is 1 kilogram, then the whole brick would weigh 2 kilograms.'

Could what Sinéad said be correct? Explain why to a friend.

> Investigate how many kilograms the brick would weigh if the weight on the left pan was 2kg, 3kg, 4kg, etc.

1. Find these.

    a) $\frac{1}{5}$ of 360°   b) $\frac{2}{3}$ of 360°   c) $\frac{5}{6}$ of 360°   d) $\frac{7}{8}$ of 360°

2. What fraction of a 360° pie chart is each of the following rotations?

    a) 40°   b) 270°   c) 225°   d) 320°

3. This pie chart shows what the preferred crisp flavour would be for 120 children. Work out from the pie chart how many children preferred each flavour.

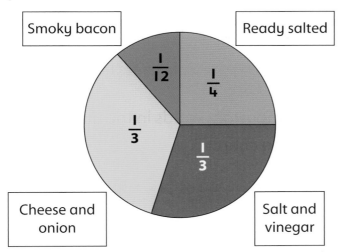

4. Construct a pie chart in your copy to illustrate the following information.

    100 people were asked to pick their favourite of 4 flowers and they responded as follows:

    Rose – 10   Tulip – 15

    Daffodil – 35   Lily – 40

Trainspotting Champions

The names of the top 120 trainspotters were recorded in a pie chart. There were representatives from Acton, Bartley, Cox, Dunbah, Echo Hill and Flynn.

How many of the top 120 came from either Acton or Cox?

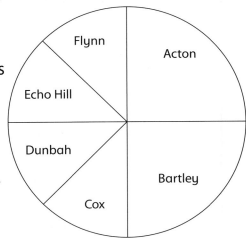

Strategy hints!

1. Look for the important words in the question.
2. Use a table or a chart.
3. Think logically.

Extension

The top 10 received awards of excellence and 1 other was selected at random to win the Choo Choo Cup trophy.

6 of the top 10 were from Flynn.

Using the chart above, what was the chance that the winner of the Choo Choo Cup trophy would also come from Flynn?

Investigate!

1. Times Table Digits

Michael makes the sequence of 2 times table numbers as far as 20 times 2.

2	4	6	8	10	12	14													

Copy and complete what Michael started. Explain how you did this to a friend.

Michael says, 'I predict that the most frequently occurring digit in this sequence, up to 20 times 2, is 1.'

Which digit do you think will be the most frequently occurring? Explain how you decided to your friend.

Michael makes a table of the frequency of the 10 digits to test what he predicted.

Digit	0	1	2	3	4	5	6	7	8	9
Frequency	4	5								

Copy and complete Michael's table.

Whose prediction was correct: yours, Michael's or neither?

Draw a pie chart of the frequency of the 10 digits shown in Michael's table.

> Investigate the frequency of digits in the 3, 4, 5, etc. times table.

2. Boys and Girls

Rachel asks everyone in her 6th class how many boys and girls are in their family.

She makes a chart of the data she collects.

Copy and complete the totals in Rachel's chart.

Explain the chart to a friend.

Write 3 questions about the chart for your friend to answer.

> Investigate every class in your school for the number of boys and girls in families.

Children in families of 6th Class
• is one child

Number of girls

Number of boys

1. Work out the area of these rectangles. Remember to record the correct unit of measurement in your answer (cm² or m²).

   a) **Rectangle 1**
   Length – 26cm
   Width – 18cm

   b) **Rectangle 2**
   Length – 34cm
   Width – 29cm

   c) **Rectangle 3**
   Length – 47m
   Width – 16m

   d) **Rectangle 4**
   Length – 14.7m
   Width – 9m

   e) **Rectangle 5**
   Length – 19.3cm
   Width – 7.6cm

   f) **Rectangle 6**
   Length – 18m
   Width – 5.47m

2. Now find the missing dimension of each of these fields.

   a) **Field 1**
   Length – ?m
   Width – 18m
   Area – 468m²

   b) **Field 2**
   Length – ?m
   Width – 24m
   Area – 840m²

   c) **Field 3**
   Length – 36m
   Width – ?m
   Area – 684m²

   d) **Field 4**
   Length – 38m
   Width – ?m
   Area – 912m²

   e) **Field 5**
   Length – ?m
   Width – 27m
   Area – 972m²

   f) **Field 6**
   Length – 42m
   Width – ?m
   Area – 1176m²

3. Fill in the blanks in the following table in your copy.

Rectangle	Perimeter	Area	Length	Width
1	176cm		38cm	
2	198cm			47cm
3		1512cm²	56cm	
4			35cm	29cm
5	324cm		53cm	
6	492cm			94cm

4. Work out the surface areas of these cubes.

a) **Cube 1**
   Edge – 14cm

b) **Cube 2**
   Edge – 17cm

c) **Cube 3**
   Edge – 23cm

d) **Cube 4**
   Edge – 29cm

e) **Cube 5**
   Edge – 35cm

f) **Cube 6**
   Edge – 38cm

5. Now work out the total surface areas of these cuboids.

a) **Cuboid 1**
   Length – 9cm
   Width – 6cm

b) **Cuboid 2**
   Length – 8cm
   Width – 7cm

c) **Cuboid 3**
   Length – 13cm
   Width – 11cm

d) **Cuboid 4**
   Length – 17cm
   Width – 12cm

e) **Cuboid 5**
   Length – 19cm
   Width – 16cm

f) **Cuboid 6**
   Length – 26cm
   Width – 18cm

Veggie Patch

Carlo wants to make the biggest veggie patch that he can.

He has 24 one-metre-long sleepers to use as a boundary.

a) What is the biggest possible veggie patch that Carlo can make with his 24 sleepers?

b) What is the 2nd biggest possible veggie patch that Carlo can make if he cannot cut any of the sleepers?

Strategy hints!

1. Look for the important words in the question.

2. Use a drawing.

3. Make a model.

Extension

a) What is the biggest possible veggie patch that Carlo can make with 80 sleepers that are each 50cm long?

b) What is the biggest possible veggie patch that Carlo can make with 40 sleepers that are each 20cm long?

Investigate!

1. A Sequence of Cuboids

Cathal makes a sequence of cuboids using 1 cm linking cubes.

 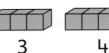

1   2   3   4   5

He numbers his cuboids.

Make Cathal's sequence of cuboids.

Explain how you did this to a friend.

Cathal says, 'Cuboid 1 has a surface area of 6 cubic centimetres.'

Is what Cathal said correct? Explain why to your friend.

Cathal draws a table of the cuboids' numbers (N) and their surface areas (A).

Cuboid number (N)	1	2	3	4	5
Surface area (A) in cm²	6				

Copy, complete and extend the table. Explain how you did this to your friend.

> Investigate the relationship between N and A.

2. Sorcha's Dotty Grids

Sorcha has lots of 1 cm squared 3x3 dotty grids.

She draws a polygon on 1 of her grids.

Copy what Sorcha did.

Explain how you did this to a friend.

How many sides does Sorcha's polygon have?

How many angles does Sorcha's polygon have?

Explain how you decided to your friend.

What is the name of Sorcha's polygon?

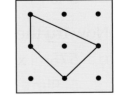

Sorcha says, 'The area of my polygon is 2cm².'

Is what Sorcha said correct? Explain why to your friend.

> Investigate the area of other polygons Sorcha could have drawn on her grids.

1. Can you write these as litres and millilitres?
   a) 1470ml
   b) 2090ml
   c) 786ml
   d) 3.4 litres
   e) 2.985 litres
   f) 9.03 litres
   g) 587ml
   h) 4.7 litres
   i) 6.218 litres

2. Fill in the gaps in your copy.

ml	l ml	l
		1.24l
7002ml		
	3l 207ml	
		0.348l
	4l 192ml	

3. Now try these. Remember to change them to the same units before you start.
   a) 7013ml + 2l 537ml + 4.74l
   b) 9.06l + 560ml + 4l 279ml
   c) 1.87l + 5l 68ml + 697ml
   d) 2l 276ml + 4.379l + 3071ml
   e) 7.418l + 6l 6ml + 2095ml
   f) 6l 57ml + 0.408l + 3273ml

4. Now try these subtraction questions, also changing capacities to the same unit first.
   a) 8l 513ml – 2.98 litres
   b) 800l ml – 6l 58ml
   c) 7.24l litres – 5467ml
   d) 9l 172ml – 4.628l
   e) 5904ml – 3.275 litres
   f) 8l 13ml – 846ml

5. Now try these.
   a) 578ml x 7
   b) 3l 745ml x 9
   c) 7.43 litres x 8
   d) 5l 94ml x 17
   e) 7483ml x 26
   f) 1.088 litres x 35

6. Now try these.
   a) 9.54 litres ÷ 6
   b) 3l 168ml ÷ 12
   c) 4284ml ÷ 9
   d) 94.4 litres ÷ 16
   e) 8l 568ml ÷ 24
   f) 6.03 l litres ÷ 37

7. There were 2.18 litres of water in Sarah's kettle. If Sarah poured 389ml of the water into her mug for a cup of tea, how much water was left in the kettle?

8. John's favourite drink is a blackcurrant juice drink. In each carton of juice there are 276ml. If John drank 38 cartons of the juice during the course of a week, how much juice did he drink in total?

Solve! .... 29. Capacity

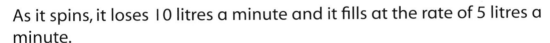

Washing Day

Mr Smedley does his washing every Saturday. His washing machine holds 45 litres of water. After filling and washing, it then goes into a rinse part of the cycle.

For 2 minutes, the machine spins and then fills with fresh water at the same time.

As it spins, it loses 10 litres a minute and it fills at the rate of 5 litres a minute.

a) 30 seconds into the rinse cycle, how much water is in the machine?

b) Mr Smedley's washing machine fills, rinses for 2 minutes, empties, fills again, then empties in a full cycle. How much water does this cycle use?

Strategy hints!

1. Look for the important words in the question.

2. Use a table or a chart.

Extension

After the spin cycle of a washing machine, the clothes in the machine still have the equivalent of 1 litre of water in them. The wet washing is put into a basket weighing 850g. The basket, when full of washing, weighs 4.7kg.

What will the clothes weigh when they are dry?

1. Three Buckets

James has 3 buckets.

He fills and empties the buckets until 1 of them holds exactly 4 litres of water.

This table is a record of what he did.

	6l Bucket	8l Bucket	11l Bucket
Step 1	0	8	0
Step 2	6	2	0
Step 3	6	0	2
Step 4	0	0	2
Step 5	0	8	2
Step 6	6	2	2
Step 7	6	0	4

Copy James's table of his records.

Explain what James did at each step to a friend.

Is what James recorded correct? Explain why to a friend.

> Investigate filling and emptying the 3 buckets in different ways so that 1 of them ends holding 2, 3, 4, etc. litres.

2. What Ciara Drinks

Ciara kept a record of what she drank on a Sunday.

This is what she did.

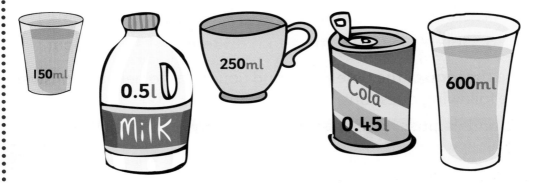

What is the total amount that Ciara drank on that Sunday?

Explain how you worked it out to a friend.

Ciara says, 'If I multiply the total amount I drank that Sunday by 365, I will have an estimate of how much I drink in 1 year.'

If Ciara did this, what would the estimate for the total amount for the year be?

Explain how you worked this out to your friend.

Is what Ciara said a reasonable thing to do? Explain why to your friend.

Investigate estimating how much you drink in 1 year.

1. Change these am/pm times to 24-hour clock times.

   a) 1:57am   b) 7:38pm   c) 12:05am   d) 11:46pm

   e) 9:25am   f) 6:21pm   g) 12:38pm   h) 9:17pm

   i) 5:55am   j) 3:15pm   k) 3:53am   l) 10:26pm

2. Use the map of the time zones and your atlas to help you answer the following questions.

   a) If it is 4:25pm in Dublin, what time is it in Moscow?

   b) If it is 10:20am in London, what time is it in New York?

   c) If it is 11:35pm in Melbourne, what time is it in Paris?

   d) If it is 5:30pm in Washington, what time is it in Los Angeles?

   e) If it is 9:05am in Rome, what time is it in Tokyo?

3. Can you work out the average speed travelled during each of these journeys?

Name	Average Speed	Time Travelling	Distance Travelled
Amy	? kph	5 hours	245km
James	? kph	6 hours	456km
Eva	? kph	9 hours	612km
Jack	? kph	4.5 hours	252km
Ruth	? kph	6.5 hours	481km

Solve!   30. Time

Travel Times

A turtle can walk 1 metre in 10 seconds.

An athlete can run 100 metres in 10 seconds.

A bullet train can travel 1 kilometre in 10 seconds.

a) How many metres, in total, will all 3 travel in 1 second?

b) How many metres, in total, will all 3 travel in 1 minute?

Strategy hints!

1. Look for the important words in the question.
2. Use a table or chart.

Extension

A train travelling at 60km per hour travels south towards another train that is travelling north at 100km per hour.

They are 20km apart.

How far apart will they be half an hour later?

Investigate!

1. Weeks, Days and Hours

Aisling has 10 digit cards | 0 | 1 | 2 | 3 | 4 | 5 | 6 | 7 | 8 | 9 | and a missing digits 'weeks, days and hours' statement.

☐ weeks ☐ days = ☐☐☐ hours

Aisling tries to choose 5 of her digits to complete the statement correctly.

This is what she did. | 2 | weeks | 1 | days = | 3 | 6 | 0 | hours

Copy what Aisling did.

Is what she did correct?
Explain why to a friend.

> Investigate different ways of completing the 'weeks, days and hours' statement correctly.

2. Stop Together

St Gabriel's Primary School has 3 different buses that stop outside the school.

The red bus stops at the school at 05:25 and then every 15 minutes.

The white bus stops at the school at 06:30 and then every 20 minutes.

The yellow bus stops at the school at 06:40 and then every 25 minutes.

Tomas says, '2 buses are due to stop together outside the school at 07:10.'

Is what Tomas said correct?
Explain why to a friend.

> Investigate times before 12 noon when more than 1 bus stops at the school.

Practise! 31. Area 2

1. Change these area amounts from m² to ares.

   a) 700m²   b) 1900m²   c) 480m²

   d) 375m²   e) 1649m²   f) 93m²

2. Calculate the area of each of the following playgrounds and then record the area in ares.

   a) **Playground 1**   b) **Playground 2**   c) **Playground 3**

   Length – 35m   Length – 45m   Length – 58m

   Width – 30m   Width – 45m   Width – 46m

   d) **Playground 4**   e) **Playground 5**   f) **Playground 6**

   Length – 124m   Length – 86m   Length –142m

   Width – 39m   Width – 48m   Width – 58m

3. Calculate the area of each of the parks and then record the area in hectares.

   a) **Park 1**   b) **Park 2**   c) **Park 3**

   Length – 125m   Length – 170m   Length – 194m

   Width – 65m   Width – 58m   Width – 46m

   d) **Park 4**   e) **Park 5**   f) **Park 6**

   Length – 218m   Length – 247m   Length – 324m

   Width – 54m   Width – 39m   Width – 68m

4. Place a cm² grid over the following shapes so that you can make a good estimate of the area of each of the shapes. Count the number of full square centimetres contained in each shape and combine the partial squares to make full square centimetres.

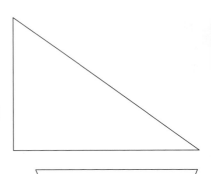

Solve!

Dogs and Cats

A cat takes 3 steps to walk the same distance that a dog can walk in 2 steps.

a) A dog and a cat start at the same point and walk 6 steps. The dog stops to let the cat catch up. How many steps does the cat need to take to catch up to the dog?

b) A cat walks 54 steps and reaches a puddle. How many steps will a dog take to reach the same puddle from the same starting point?

Strategy hints!

1. Look for the important words in the question.
2. Use a table or a chart.
3. Think logically.

Extension

A small dog takes 5 steps to walk the same distance that a large dog can walk in 2 steps.

They take steps at the same time and walk around a 100m track.

How many metres has the small dog walked when the large dog has completed 2 laps of the track?

1. Seán's Garden

Seán designs his garden with 4 identical rectangles.

The perimeter of each rectangle is 24 metres.

He uses his 4 rectangles to surround a green lawn.

Draw a copy of Seán's garden.

Explain how you did this to a friend.

Seán says, 'The area of the green lawn is 16m².'

Could what Seán said be correct?

Explain why to your friend.

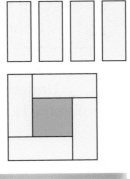

> Investigate what other areas Seán's lawn could be.

2. Sive's Sequence of Triangles

Sive draws the first 5 shapes in a sequence of triangles in centimetre square grids.

She gives each shape a number name.

N(1) N(2) N(3) N(4) N(5)

Copy, complete and extend Sive's sequence.

Describe what is special about Sive's sequence of triangles to a friend.

Sive makes a table of the data for the sequence of the number of each shape (N), the length of the side of each large grid (L), the area of each grid (S) and the area of each triangle (T).

Number of shape (N)	1	2	3	4	5				
Length of square in cm (L)	2	3	4	5	6				
Area of square in cm² (S)	4								
Area of triangle in cm² (T)	1.5								

Copy, complete and extend the data in Sive's table.

Describe the table to your friend.

> Investigate patterns and relationships in the data about the sequence.

The 9 Problem-Solving Strategies

1 Look for the important words in the question

Write them down.
Underline them.
Make sure I know what to do.

2 Look for a pattern

Can I see something happening over and over again?
Will this help me solve the problem?

3 Have a go

Try an answer.
Does the answer make sense?

4 Use a table or chart

Would something like this help?

5 Use a drawing

Can I draw something about the problem?
Will this help me to find the answer?

6 Work backwards

Can I start at the end of the question to help work it out?
Will my answer work?

7 Try an easier problem

Can I change the numbers in the question to make it simpler?
Will this make finding the answer easier?

8 Make a model

Can I use paper or blocks to help me find the answer?
Can I use people to help me find the answer?

9 Think logically

Can I tell something about the answer straight away?
Can I get rid of answers that are not correct?

SAY NO TO BULLYING
NOBODY DESERVES TO BE BULLIED
TELL AN ADULT YOU CAN TRUST

This Anti-Bullying campaign is supported by the Department of Education and Skills with the co-operation of the Irish Educational Publishers Association